Core Knowledge Language Arts®

Unit 6
Workbook

Skills Strand
KINDERGARTEN

Amplify learning.

Core Knowledge®

ISBN 978-1-61700-178-9

Printed in the USA
NA05 LSCOW 2017

Unit 6
Workbook

This Workbook contains worksheets that accompany many of the lessons from the Teacher Guide for Unit 6. Each worksheet is identified by the lesson number in which it is used. The worksheets in this book do not include written instructions for students because the instructions would have words that are not decodable. Teachers will explain these worksheets to the students orally, using the instructions in the Teacher Guide. The Workbook is a student component, which means each student should have a Workbook.

Dear Family Member,

Ask your child to cut out the letter cards. Show the cards to your child and have him or her say the sounds, not the letter names. Arrange the cards to make the words "skin," "sun," "spin," "kin," "snip," "nut," "not," "net," "stun," "skip," "step," "stop," "spot," "sit," "sip," "set," "pet," "pot," "pun," "tip," "top," and "pit," and have your child read the words. Additional Activity: Say one of the words listed above and ask your child to try and spell the word by selecting and arranging letter cards.

n	k	s
u	o	t
i	e	p

1. ___ ___

2. ___ ___ ___

3. ___ ___ ___

4. ___ ___ ___ ___

5. ___ ___ ___ ___

Directions: Have students write the dictated words.

6. _____ _____ _____

7. _____ _____ _____

8. _____ _____ _____

9. _____ _____ _____ _____

10. _____ _____ _____

frog	crab	flag
drum	stem	steps

stem   drum   crab

steps   frog   flag

Directions: Have stude

| twig | spot | swim |
| stop | plug | grin |

_____

- - - - - - - - - -

_____

_____

- - - - - - - - - -

_____

as	his
is	has

Directions: Have students complete each sentence.

1. Stan _____ mad at Fred.

2. Jim _____ not met Tim.

3. Ted is _____ dad.

4. Jen is not as sad _____ Kim.

Name _____

Dear Family Member,

This is a story your child has read at school. Encourage your child to read the story aloud to you and talk about the events in the story. If your child has difficulty reading a word, encourage your child to blend the word letter by letter to read it.

Kit can swim.

Kit can flip and flop.

Kit can skip.

Kit can run.

During the first few months of school, we have focused on teaching your child the specific sounds associated with each letter. Students must know these sounds in order to blend and read words. We will now turn our attention to learning the names of each letter so your child is able to recite the names of the letters in alphabetical order.

Point to each letter below and ask your child to say each letter name with you. If you like, you can sing the ABC song with your child as you point to each letter. Make sure to say the name of each letter clearly, especially if you are singing the ABC song. In class, we clap after the letters, 'l', 'm', 'n', 'o', and 'p'. this helps children avoid thinking 'lmnop' is a word.

legs	pots	jets	pens
rats	bags	beds	hats

/s/ as in cat<u>s</u>

/z/ as in dog<u>s</u>

Directions: Have students write the words that end in 's' pronounced /s/ under the /s/ header and the words that end in 's' pronounced /z/ under the 'z' header.

rubs	taps	hits	sips
wins	sits	begs	tugs

/s/ as in nap<u>s</u>

_____

- - - - - - - - - - - - - -

_____

- - - - - - - - - - - - - -

_____

_____

_____

- - - - - - - - - - - - - -

/z/ as in run<u>s</u>

_____

- - - - - - - - - - - - - -

_____

- - - - - - - - - - - - - -

_____

_____

_____

_____

Dear Family Member,

On the front and back of this page, have your child copy each word under the matching picture. If necessary, identify the pictures for your child.

1. cans

_____

- -

_____

2. desk

_____

- -

_____

3. pigs

_____

- -

_____

4. crab

_____

- - - - - - - - - - - - -

_____

5. gift

_____

- - - - - - - - - - - - -

_____

6. hand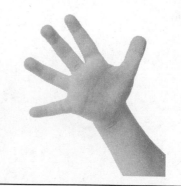

_____

- - - - - - - - - - - - -

_____

Dear Family Member,

Your child has been taught to read words with four sounds. These words contain consonant clusters, i.e., two consonant spellings that stand next to each other in a word. Consonant clusters are difficult to read at first. Encourage your child to read the words by first saying the individual sounds and then blending the sounds to make words. Ask your child to cut out the two circles. Pin the smaller circle on top of the larger circle with a brass fastener. Ask your child to spin the smaller circle to make words. Have your child read the words he or she makes.

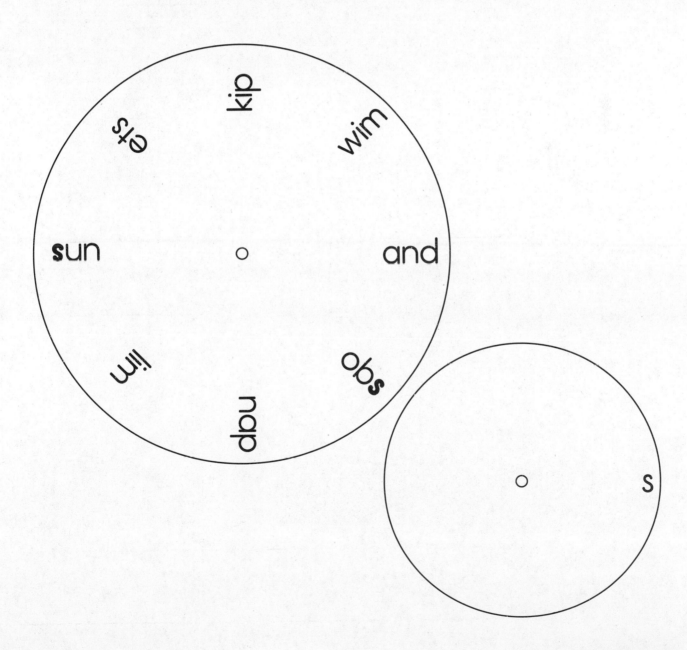

Name _____

Dear Family Member,

This is a story your child has read at school. Encourage your child to read the story aloud to you and talk about the events in the story. If your child has difficulty reading a word, encourage your child to blend the word letter by letter to read it.

Kit ran and hid.

Stan ran and got Kit.

Stan ran and hid.

Kit ran and got Stan.

Kit and Stan had fun.

Continue practicing singing the letter names using the chart below.

a	b	c	d
e	f	g	h
i	j	k	l
m	n	o	p
q	r	s	t
u	v	w	x
y	z		

1. _____ _____ _____
   - - - - - - - - - - - - - - -
   _____ _____ _____

2. _____ _____ _____
   - - - - - - - - - - - - - - -
   _____ _____ _____

3. _____ _____ _____
   - - - - - - - - - - - - - - -
   _____ _____ _____

4. _____ _____ _____
   - - - - - - - - - - - - - - -
   _____ _____ _____

5. _____ _____ _____ _____
   - - - - - - - - - - - - - - - - - - -
   _____ _____ _____ _____

Directions: Have students write the dictated words.

6. _____

7. _____

8. _____

9. _____

10. _____

Dear Family Member,

This is a story your child has read at school. Encourage your child to read the story aloud to you and talk about the events in the story. If your child has difficulty reading a word, encourage your child to blend the word letter by letter to read it.

Kit ha**s** hats.

Kit ha**s** big hats.

Kit ha**s** flat hats.

Kit ha**s** fun hats.

Point to each letter and ask your child to provide the sound of the letter first and then the letter name. If your child has difficulty, you may want to make flash cards of these letters and practice a few each night.

Name _____

Dear Family Member,

On the front and back of the worksheet have your child draw a line from each word on the left to the matching picture. If necessary, identify the pictures for your child.

1. stamp

2. vest

3. steps

4. lamp

© 2013 Core Knowledge Foundation

5. plant

6. nest

7. belt

8. pants

9. mask

Dear Family Member,

This is a story your child has read at school. Encourage your child to read the story aloud to you and talk about the events in the story. If your child has difficulty reading a word, encourage your child to blend the word letter by letter to read it.

Kit ha**s** cats.

Kit's cats run fast.

Kit's cats lap up milk.

Kit's cats jump up on Kit's bed.

Point to each letter and ask your child to provide the sound of the letter first and then provide the letter name. If your child has difficulty, you may want to make flash cards of these letters and practice a few each night.

g   j   d

y   x   f

r

k   e

u

c   b

Dear Family Member,

This is a story your child has read at school. Encourage your child to read the story aloud to you and talk about the events in the story. If your child has difficulty reading a word, encourage your child to blend the word letter by letter to read it.

Kit's mom gets up at six.

Kit's mom gets dad up.
Kit's mom gets Kit up.

Kit's mom gets dad fed.
Kit's mom gets Kit fed.
Kit's mom gets Kit's pets fed.

Have your child sing the ABC song and write the missing letters as she sings.

a   b   ___   d

e   f   g   h

___   j   k   l

___   n   o   p

q   r   s   ___

u   v   ___   x

y   z

Name _____

Dear Family Member,

This is a story your child has read at school. Encourage your child to read the story aloud to you and talk about the events in the story. If your child has difficulty reading a word, encourage your child to blend the word letter by letter to read it.

Kit had red pants.
Kit's pants got lost at
camp.

Kit's mom got mad at Kit.
Kit's mom can't stand
lost pants.

Have your child sing the ABC song and write the missing letters as she sings.

a   ___   c   d

e   ___   g   h

i   ___   k   l

___   n   o   p

___   r   s   t

u   ___   w   x

y   ___

milk	fist	stump
cast	crust	tent

Directions: Have students write each word under its matching picture.

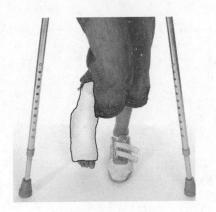

_____

_____

_____

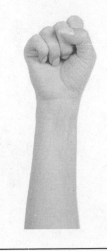

_____

_____

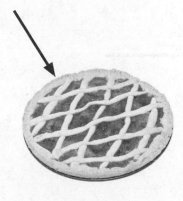

_____

| crib | jump | bugs |
| lamp | kids | stamp |

_____

_____

_____

_____

Dear Family Member,

This is a story your child has read at school. Encourage your child to read the story aloud to you and talk about the events in the story. If your child has difficulty reading a word, encourage your child to blend the word letter by letter to read it.

Kit ha**s** mumps.
Kit **is** in bed.
Kit can't get up.

Kit can't run and jump.
Kit can't skip and hop.
Kit **is** sad.

Sing the ABC song with your child encouraging him to write each letter on the blank. Be sure your child writes lower case letters, in alphabetical order.

____ ____ ____ ____ ____ ____ ____

____ ____ ____ ____ ____ ____ ____

____ ____ ____ ____ ____ ____ ____

____ ____ ____ ____ ____

Dear Family Member,

Your child has been taught to read words with four and five letters. These words contain consonant clusters, i.e., two consonant spellings that stand next to each other in a word. Encourage your child to read the words by first saying the individual sounds and then blending the sounds to make words. Help your child cut out the word cards. Show the cards to your child and have your child read them aloud. You may also read the words aloud and have your child write the sounds down, one at a time. Please keep these cards for future practice. Note: the 's' is bolded in some words because it is pronounced /z/. Your child has learned about this in class.

skip	clips	frog**s**
helps	swim	rest
stamp	plan**s**	tag**s**
spot	fast	print

1.   d   a   b

2.   h   f   i

3.   x   k   q

4.   g   y   j

5.   w   n   m

6.   e   c   o

Directions: Have students circle the dictated letters.

7.   o   a   c

8.   j   f   y

9.   h   r   m

10.   u   n   v

11.   p   d   g

12.   q   k   t

Directions: For each pair of words spoken, have students circle the smiley face if the words rhyme and the frowny face if the words do not rhyme.

1.

2.

3.

4.

5.

6.

Student Record Sheet Unit 6 Assessment

	Word						Total Phonemes Correct
1.	fist	/f/	/i/	/s/	/t/		_____(4)
2.	plum	/p/	/l/	/u/	/m/		_____ (4)
3.	step	/s/	/t/	/e/	/p/		_____ (4)
4.	plant	/p/	/l/	/a/	/n/	/t/	_____ (5)
5.	drop	/d/	/r/	/o/	/p/		_____ (4)
6.	help	/h/	/e/	/l/	/p/		_____ (4)
7.	crust	/c/	/r/	/u/	/s/	/t/	_____ (5)
8.	swim	/s/	/w/	/i/	/m/		_____ (4)
9.	sand	/s/	/a/	/n/	/d/		_____ (4)
10.	spot	/s/	/p/	/o/	/t/		_____ (4)

Initial Clusters_____/7   Final Clusters_____/5   Total Correct _____/42

☺ fat   cat   mat   hat

1. fit   hit   mist   fist

2. glum   plum   punt   bum

3. stop   stub   stab   step

4. plan   pant   plant   plug

5. drop   drip   drug   drab

6.   hip   held   help   helm

7. crank   rust   crisp   crust

8. swum   swam   swig   swim

9. stand   sand   stab   sad

10. spot   spit   spat   spam

TOTAL POINTS: ____/10

1. twig

2. crab

3. pond

4. desk

5. frog

Directions: Draw a line from each word on the left to the matching picture.

Directions: On the front and back of this page, have the student copy each word under the matching picture. If necessary, identify the pictures.

1. nest

2. tent

3. lamp

4. plant

_____

- - - - - - - - - - - - - -

_____

5. mask

_____

- - - - - - - - - - - - - -

_____

6. sled

_____

- - - - - - - - - - - - - -

_____

| bugs | drops | clips | plums |
| lamps | sleds | lists | bands |

/s/ as in cat<u>s</u>

/z/ as in dog<u>s</u>

Directions: Have students write the words with the plural marker 's' pronounced /s/ under the /s/ header and the words with the plural marker 's' pronounced /z/ under the 'z' header.

clams	nests	twins	crops
drums	ramps	hands	tents

/s/ as in cat̲s

/z/ as in dog̲s

Name _____

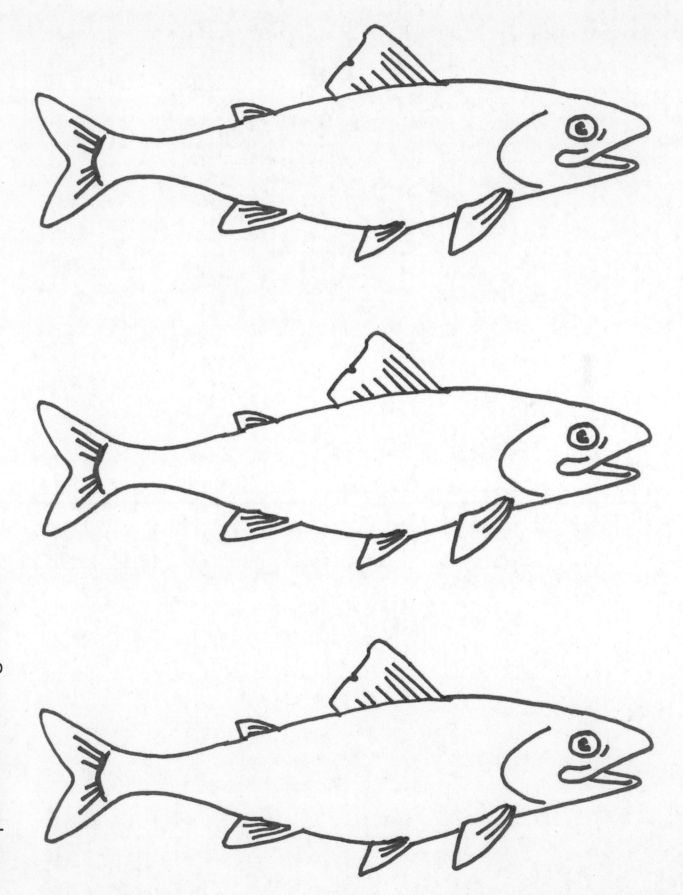

Template for Fishing Pond

Directions: Have students cut out the word cards and place them on the matching words on Worksheet PP4.

clamp	bump	sled
stamp	crust	crop
frog	desk	trips
blast	drums	beds
split	twins	winds

Name _____

Directions: Have students read the word cards from Worksheet PP3 and place them on top of the matching words on this worksheet.

stamp	crop	twins
blast	bump	frog
split	clamp	trips
crust	sled	desk
beds	winds	drums

Template for Game Board with Decodable Words

Dear Family Member,

Help your child cut out the two circles. Pin the smaller circle on top of the larger circle with a brass fastener. Ask your child to spin the smaller circle to make words. Have your child read the words he or she makes.

TAKE HOME

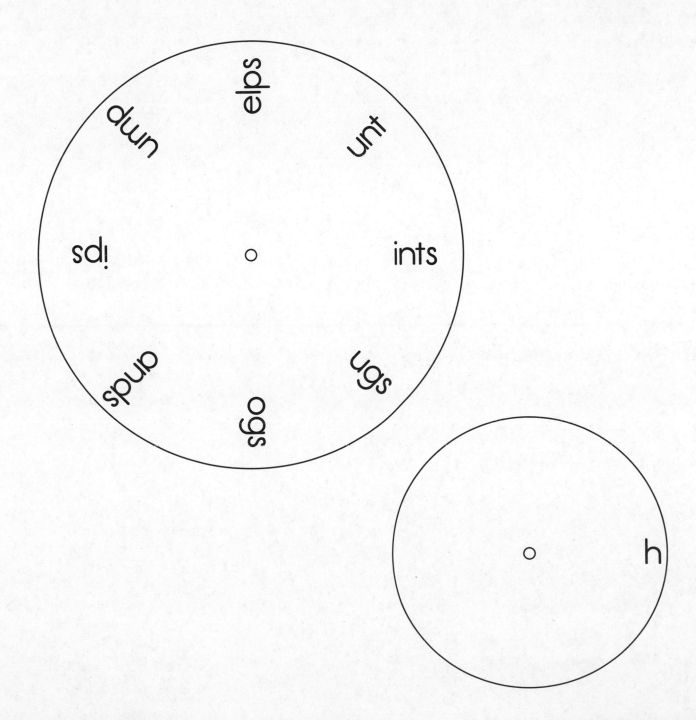

Running Record for "Pip's Cats" – As student reads aloud from the Reader, Kit, *mark any misread words directly above the word; circle any omitted words.*

Pip's Cats

Pip is Kit's pal.

Pip has six cats.

Pip's cats got in the mud.

Pip's cats left mud on his rug.

Pip's mom got mad.

Number of misread words: _____/25

Notes:

Running Record for "Vic Gets Lost"– As student reads aloud from the Reader, Kit, *mark any misread words directly above the word; circle any omitted words.*

Vic Gets Lost

Pip's cat Vic got lost.

Pip felt sad.

Kit ran and got Vic.

Kit set Vic on Pip's lap.

Pip felt glad.

Number of misread words: _____/22

Notes:

Kit's pal Fred gulps hi**s** milk.
Fast Fred gulps and gulps.
Fred gets milk on hi**s** desk.
Fred gets milk on hi**s** pants.

Fred gets milk on Kit.
Kit gets mad at Fred.
"Stop it, Fred!"

Directions: Have students trace and copy the letters. Encourage students to say the sounds while writing the letters.

i

i

r

r

j

j

k

k

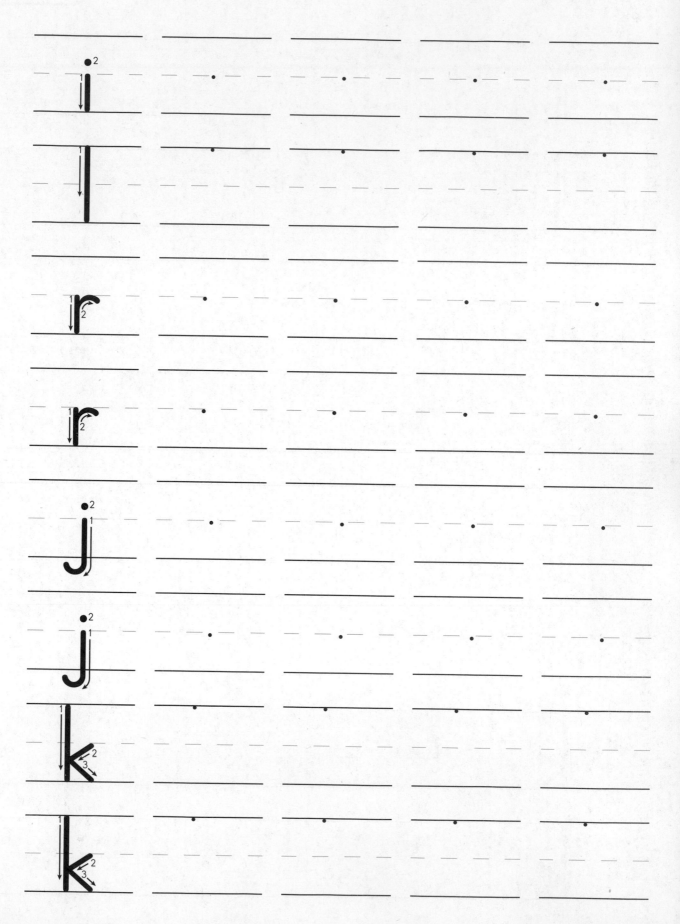

Directions: Have students trace and copy the letters. Encourage students to say the sounds while writing the letters.

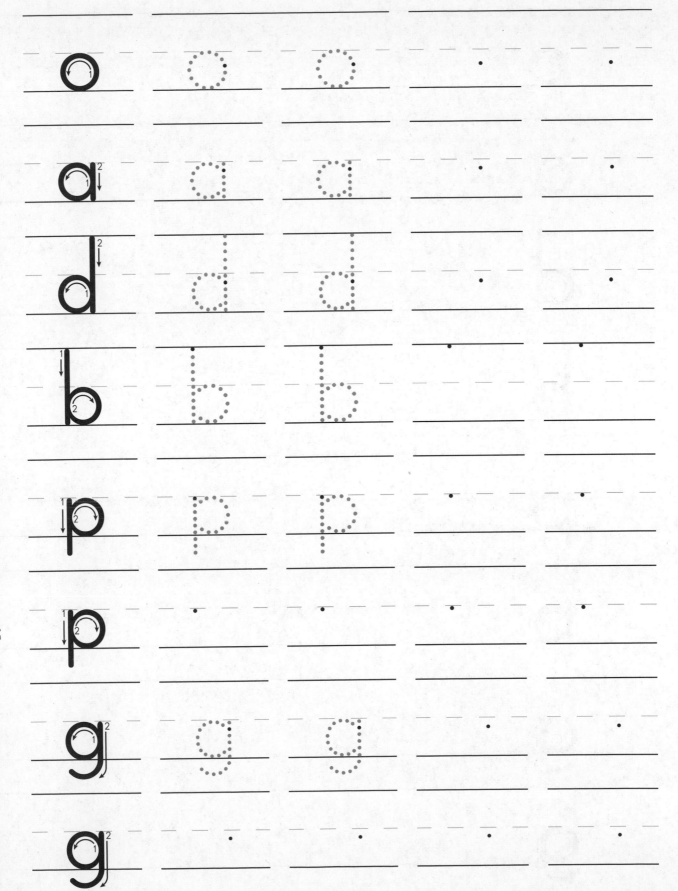

© 2013 Core Knowledge Foundation

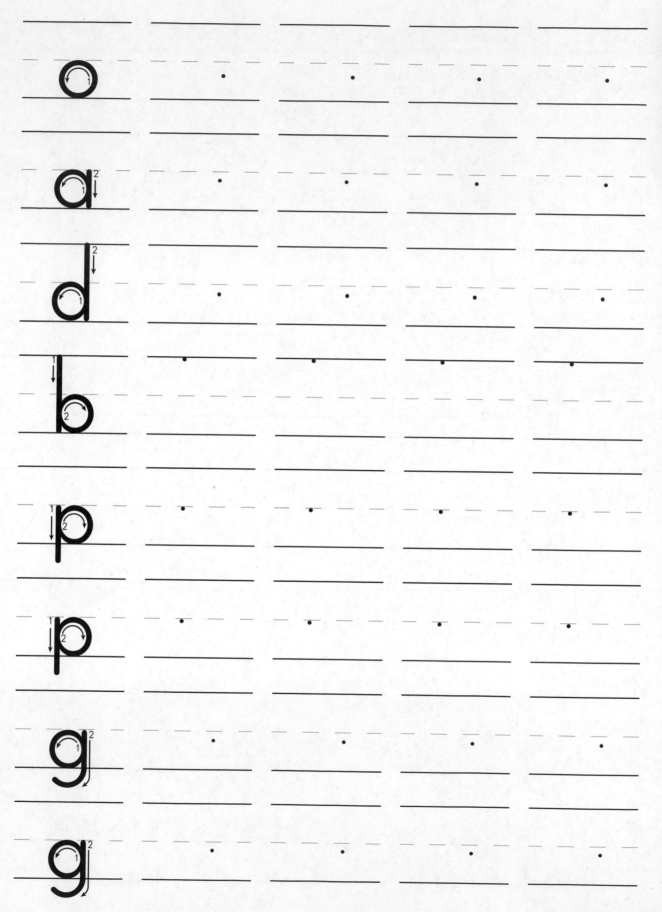

Directions: Have students trace and copy the letters. Encourage students to say the sounds while writing the letters.

plum

skip

clap

slip

drip

flat

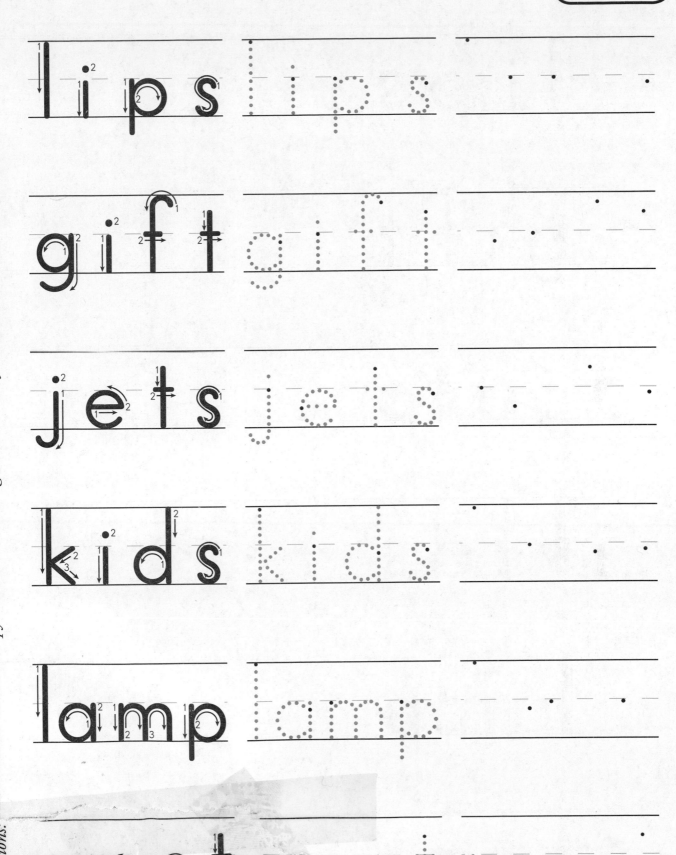

Directions: Have students trace and copy the letters. Encourage students to say the sounds while writing the letters.

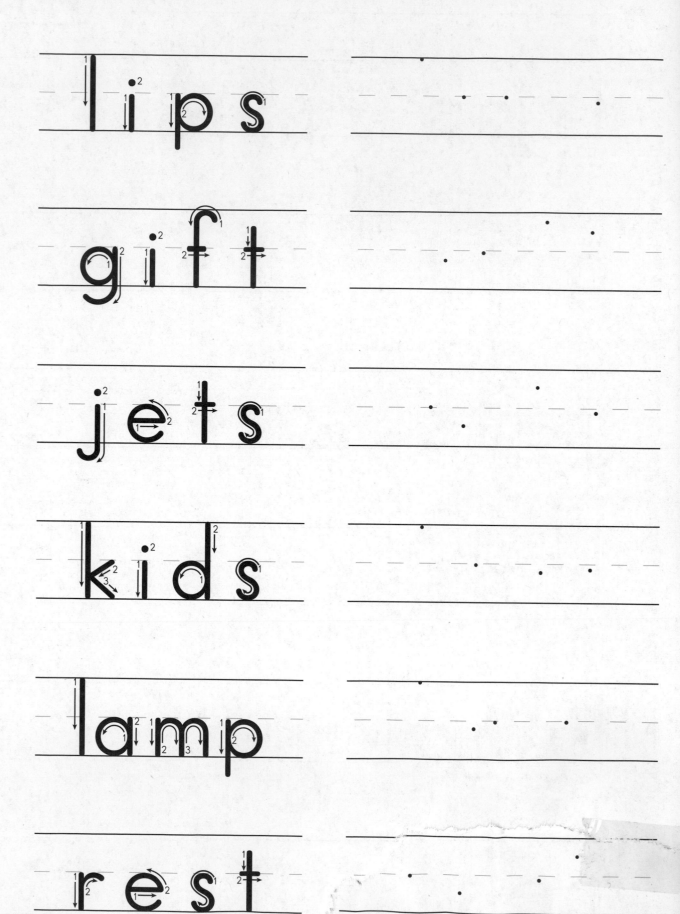

lips

gift

jets

kids

lamp

rest

crisp

plant

slump

drops

twigs

belts

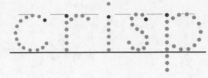

crisp

plant

slump

 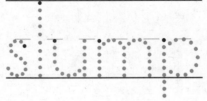 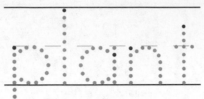

drops

 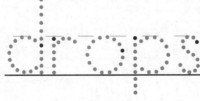 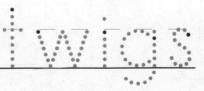

twigs

belts

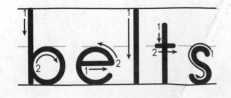 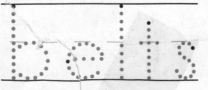

Directions: Have students trace and copy the letters. Encourage students to say the sounds while writing the letters.

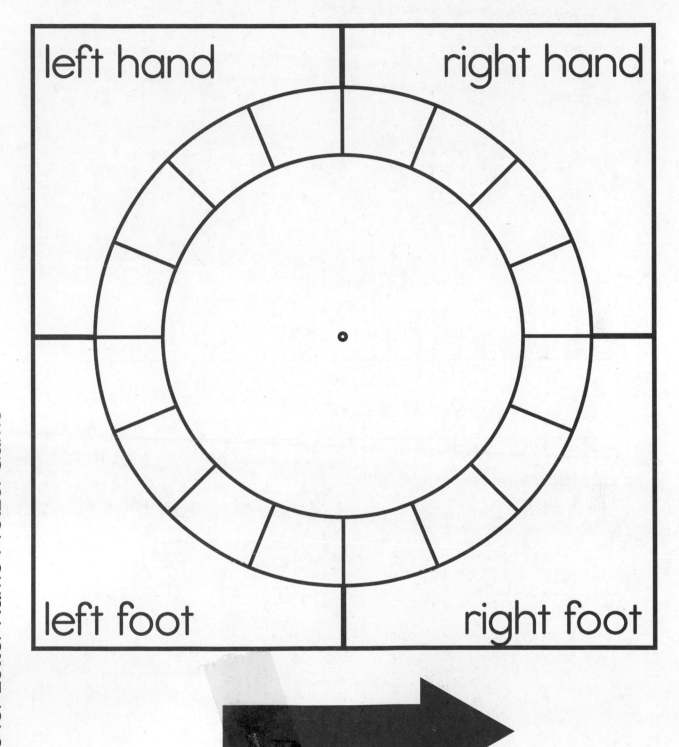

left hand

right hand

left foot

right foot

Template for Letter Name Pretzel Game

1. hot   bug

2. bed   can

3. sit   pot

4. hug   red

5. man   fit

6. bump   trip

7. test   land

8. spent   grump

9. stand   tent

10. flip   best

Core Knowledge Language Arts

Series Editor-in-Chief
E. D. Hirsch, Jr.

President
Linda Bevilacqua

Editorial Staff
Carolyn Gosse, Senior Editor - Preschool
Khara Turnbull, Materials Development Manager
Michelle L. Warner, Senior Editor - Listening & Learning

Mick Anderson
Robin Blackshire
Maggie Buchanan
Paula Coyner
Sue Fulton
Sara Hunt
Erin Kist
Robin Luecke
Rosie McCormick
Cynthia Peng
Liz Pettit
Ellen Sadler
Deborah Samley
Diane Auger Smith
Sarah Zelinke

Design and Graphics Staff
Scott Ritchie, Creative Director

Kim Berrall
Michael Donegan
Liza Greene
Matt Leech
Bridget Moriarty
Lauren Pack

Consulting Project Management Services
ScribeConcepts.com

Additional Consulting Services
Ang Blanchette
Dorrit Green
Carolyn Pinkerton

Acknowledgments

These materials are the result of the work, advice, and encouragement of numerous individuals over many years. Some of those singled out here already know the depth of our gratitude; others may be surprised to find themselves thanked publicly for help they gave quietly and generously for the sake of the enterprise alone. To helpers named and unnamed we are deeply grateful.

Contributors to Earlier Versions of these Materials
Susan B. Albaugh, Kazuko Ashizawa, Nancy Braier, Kathryn M. Cummings, Michelle De Groot, Diana Espinal, Mary E. Forbes, Michael L. Ford, Ted Hirsch, Danielle Knecht, James K. Lee, Diane Henry Leipzig, Martha G. Mack, Liana Mahoney, Isabel McLean, Steve Morrison, Juliane K. Munson, Elizabeth B. Rasmussen, Laura Tortorelli, Rachael L. Shaw, Sivan B. Sherman, Miriam E. Vidaver, Catherine S. Whittington, Jeannette A. Williams

We would like to extend special recognition to Program Directors Matthew Davis and Souzanne Wright who were instrumental to the early development of this program.

Schools
We are truly grateful to the teachers, students, and administrators of the following schools for their willingness to field test these materials and for their invaluable advice: Capitol View Elementary, Challenge Foundation Academy (IN), Community Academy Public Charter School, Lake Lure Classical Academy, Lepanto Elementary School, New Holland Core Knowledge Academy, Paramount School of Excellence, Pioneer Challenge Foundation Academy, New York City PS 26R (The Carteret School), PS 30X (Wilton School), PS 50X (Clara Barton School), PS 96Q, PS 102X (Joseph O. Loretan), PS 104Q (The Bays Water), PS 214K (Michael Friedsam), PS 223Q (Lyndon B. Johnson School), PS 308K (Clara Cardwell), PS 333Q (Goldie Maple Academy), Sequoyah Elementary School, South Shore Charter Public School, Spartanburg Charter School, Steed Elementary School, Thomas Jefferson Classical Academy, Three Oaks Elementary, West Manor Elementary.

And a special thanks to the CKLA Pilot Coordinators Anita Henderson, Yasmin Lugo-Hernandez, and Susan Smith, whose suggestions and day-to-day support to teachers using these materials in their classrooms was critical.

CREDITS